Raise the Bar

Initial to Grade 2

Guitar

Teaching Notes written
by Anders Rye

Published by
Trinity College London Press
trinitycollege.com

Registered in England
Company no. 09726123

Printed in England by Caligraving Ltd.

Contents

Teaching Notes – Initial

Allemande (Gervaise)

An *allemande* is a German dance from the Renaissance or Baroque era. Music from that period was often grouped in suites with the *allemande* as one of the movements. Not much is known about Claude Gervaise although he was probably a court musician under King Francis I, and his most important work is *Suites de Danses* from 1557.

The melody consists of two four-bar phrases with each phrase repeated, so adding dynamics would give some colour and contrast to the music. The first note of the first phrase is a dotted crotchet so be careful with the timing and make sure you hold the note for its full value. Keep the phrasing legato and take extra care with the quavers so they don't sound detached and 'choppy', especially when changing back and forth between C and D. You could perhaps use those two notes as a separate legato exercise as preparation for the whole piece.

Study in A Minor (Cano)

Antonio Cano was a Spanish composer and a pupil of Dionisio Aguado. Cano made a significant contribution to the guitar literature, composing about a hundred pieces and exercises and publishing his *Método de Guitarra* in 1852. It is likely that he also taught Francisco Tárrega and contributed to the development of the tremolo technique.

This study consists of two repeated eight-bar sections. It is a good exercise in playing music in two parts and using fingers and thumb together. You should aim for a relaxed picking hand position where you can use fingers and thumb without having to move your hand. Also, try to keep your thumb in front of your index finger so they don't get in each other's way, as the thumb plays downwards and the fingers upwards. It is important to let the bass notes ring for the whole bar for most of the piece, though you must be careful not to let the E and A overlap at the end of each section. Make sure there is a good balance between fingers and thumb and that the melody is clear and smooth throughout.

Morning (Grieg)

This piece is taken from the work *Peer Gynt* (1875) by Norwegian composer Edvard Grieg, and was originally composed to accompany the play of the same name by Henrik Ibsen. Some of the music from *Peer Gynt* has been widely used in film, TV and cartoons, as well as being covered in styles ranging from jazz to heavy metal.

The melody is eight bars long and is first played with the thumb, then repeated an octave higher with the fingers. Watch out for the fingering in bar 6 and make the position change towards the end as fluent as possible. The original title of this piece is actually *Morning Mood* and, as the title suggests, depicts a beautiful sunrise in the Moroccan desert. Try to keep this in mind and make it as graceful and elegant as you can, adding crescendo and diminuendo for colour and intensity.

Dance of the Islands (Lambert)

Florian Lambert is a songwriter, educator and poet from Quebec, Canada. In addition to classical guitar teaching, educational activities in schools and composing songs, he hosted a series of television programmes devoted to young song writers.

The present piece looks quite long but it is essentially just two eight-bar sections that are repeated with the first section being played again at the end. The $\frac{3}{4}$ time signature is often used for dances (such as the waltz) and has a characteristic 'lilt' to it, which is achieved by accenting the first beat of each bar.

The piece should be played with some pace to keep the melody flowing, however it can be tricky to play music in two parts so make sure you keep the melody clear and legato while still controlling the bass notes with the thumb. Your picking hand should be in a position where you can comfortably use both fingers and thumb without really having to move your hand much. You could perhaps use open strings as an exercise to practise the picking pattern before you tackle the whole piece.

Handbells (Ryan)

Gary Ryan is a critically acclaimed guitarist and a Fellow of the Royal College of Music. He has performed all over the world and is widely respected as an adjudicator and composer. He has written many pieces for guitar, several of which have been used as grade pieces over the years.

Handbells is made up of four phrases with the second phrase being a variation of the first, and the fourth phrase a variation of third. It is a challenging piece because you have to let the notes ring as much as possible. The C in the bass is difficult to hold while playing the melody so make sure your fingers are arched over the strings. Check your thumb position behind the neck and lower it if you have problems reaching over the strings and holding the bass note.

First Steps (Tromp)

First Steps is taken from the book *String Fingers* by Barend Tromp, which is a collection of easy pieces for guitar. Tromp is a Dutch guitarist and composer who is also head of a music school in Weert.

This is another piece in $\frac{3}{4}$ which uses both fingers and thumbs, similar to *Dance of the Islands*. Although it is important to leave many of the notes ringing, you have to be careful not to let the bass notes ring together and make the sound muddy. This is particularly difficult when changing from a higher to a lower string, for example in bars 2-3 where you are switching from D to E. It is tricky to stop the D from ringing as you play E but it can be done using either (1) your picking hand index finger or a free fretting hand finger, or (2) playing the E first and muting the D with the thumb immediately after. It is easier to change from a lower to a higher string, for example bars 12-13, where you can use the side of your thumb to mute the lower string.

As a bass muting exercise, try alternating back and forth between the open bass strings with your thumb, aiming to make the change sound smooth and legato but without leaving a noticeable gap either. This is probably harder than it sounds but muting the bass strings is a technique that you will often come across so it is well worth practising.

Clouds (Nash)

John Nash is a guitarist and composer based in Ventnor on the Isle of Wight. He has worked mainly as a peripatetic guitar teacher in inner London and Isle of Wight schools and also in adult education. He is passionate about saving special landscapes, such as Walthamstow Marshes in the Lea Valley, from destruction.

Clouds is based on arpeggios and has a rather melancholy feel. The picking hand is playing *tirando* throughout so it requires a relaxed position where thumb and fingers move freely without too much movement of the wrist. Try to let the notes ring as much as possible and make sure you can play the piece fluently and in time before adding the dynamics. There is a lot of dynamic variation, which adds character and intensity to the piece but take care not to speed up or slow down during crescendos/diminuendos; only the volume should change, not the tempo.

Greensleeves (Trad.)

Greensleeves is a traditional English folk song dating from the 15th or 16th century, and would have been played on the lute in its day. The song refers to a 'Lady Greensleeves' and while many believe that the lyrics were written by Henry VIII to Anne Boleyn, this has actually never been proven. In fact, the song is composed in an Italian style which only reached England after Henry's death so this suggests that it is from a later period.

This song basically consists of two different eight-bar sections of melody, where each section is repeated with a variation at the end. It is in $\frac{3}{4}$ so remember to accent beat one to give it a lilting feel and count carefully to keep the syncopations in time. The change from G#–F#–G# needs to be connected and smooth so you may have to let your thumb move down slightly behind the neck in order to reach the F# with finger 4. Also note that the A in bar 8 is played with finger 3, not finger 2 as the beginning.

Allemande

arr. Lee Sollory

Claude Gervaise
(c. 1500–c. 1560)

Study in A Minor

Edited by Norman Vaux

Antonio Cano
(1811–1897)

Morning

arr. Lee Sollory

Edvard Grieg
(1843-1907)

Dance of the Islands

Florian Lambert
(b. 1942)

Handbells

Gary Ryan
(b. 1969)

First Steps

Barend Tromp
(b. 1971)

Clouds

John Nash
(b. 1948)

Greensleeves

Edited by Norman Vaux

Traditional

Teaching Notes – Grade 1

Andante (Carulli)

Ferdinando Carulli was born in Naples, Italy in 1770 and was one of the most prolific composers for guitar, as well as a gifted and celebrated performer. He composed over 400 works for guitar and wrote the *Méthode complète pour guitare ou lyre* which is still used. Andante is taken from the *Méthode complète pour parvenir a pincer la guitare*, which was published in 1830. This piece originally contained a second part which has been omitted for this book.

Andante (meaning walking pace) consists of three eight-bar sections where the last section is the same as the first and each section has four phrases. There are two different musical patterns in each phrase. The first pattern consists of single note quavers played with alternating fingers; the second pattern is parallel thirds with a bass note in between. Try to keep the picking even and balanced when you switch between the two. The phrases are all very similar so make good use of dynamics to give contrast and colour.

Allegro (Giuliani)

Mauro Giuliani was an early 19th century Italian guitar virtuoso who became a musical celebrity and toured all over Europe. He lived in Vienna for a few years, where he began publishing his own compositions as well as teaching guitar. This *Allegro* (meaning fast) is taken from a work named *Le Papillon*.

Much of this piece is based on the arpeggio pattern on the first two beats. Keep your picking hand relaxed and start by placing thumb and fingers on the individual strings. Make sure that each finger stays on the same string. Only the thumb should be moving between strings. Practise the pattern slowly at first until you get the hang of it, keep it even and hold the notes as a chord for as long as you can. The arpeggio pattern changes at the end but try to keep the fretting hand movement to a minimum as you switch between the Am and E chords. See if you can avoid letting the A and E bass notes ring over each other. This is easier said than done but it is possible using your thumb or a fretting hand finger, or a combination of both, to stop unwanted notes from ringing.

Andantino op. 59 (Carcassi)

Matteo Carcassi was born in Florence, Italy in 1792 and was a much celebrated guitarist and teacher. Some of his most famous compositions include *25 Etudes* and *Méthode Complete* for guitar from which this piece is taken.

Andantino can confusingly mean both slower or faster than andante, depending on the period in which the piece was written, so the tempo marking should taken as a guide only. This piece has two repeated sections and the last four bars of the second section are the same as the first section. Aim to keep a good balance between voices and feel free to experiment with dynamics and tone, particularly on the repeats. This could perhaps mean playing some parts ponticello or sul tasto for variation in timbre.

Humoresque (Benham)

Humoresque is taken from Patrick Benham's book *7 Easy Guitar Solos* from 1984. Benham is a renowned teacher in Bristol and has published several compositions for guitar.

A humoresque is usually a short and lively composition, good humoured in mood rather than humorous. The melody here is quite simple, almost like a children's song, and the bass has a melody line of its own as well as providing the harmony. Imagine this as a choral piece where you have to bring out both voices together as a harmony (vertically) and as a melody (horizontally) but keep them well balanced as you move across the strings. Also make sure you hold the notes on the first beat of bars 11 and 13 as you play the open G string.

The Hugh Christie Pieces IV (Twigg)

Hugh Christie was the son of a city merchant, founder member of the National Farmers Union and also involved in the formation of the Women's Institute. He has a school in Tonbridge named after him and was awarded an OBE for political and public services in Kent.

The main feature in this piece is known as pedal point. This is where a note is sustained or repeated, thereby creating harmonic tension (dissonance) and release (consonance) against the other notes. It is usually played in the bass so it is more appropriate to use the term 'inverted pedal point' for this piece as the pedal note is the top E string.

The pedal note can be played using the same finger or alternating fingers but all the movement is by the thumb in the bass. In fact, keep a good strong bass line throughout and make sure that the pedal note is even and not too dominant. This piece has to be played with some pace so keep your picking hand relaxed and pay close attention to any dynamic changes. Pedal point limits the harmonic possibilities somewhat and can make the music sound quite repetitive so dynamics are an important way to add contrast and intensity. The semiquavers may look intimidating at first but the technique is actually not so difficult to master and get up to speed. Try using the first bar as an exercise to build fluency and speed, and hold the notes for as long as possible.

Cachucha (Lindsey-Clark)

Cachucha is a Spanish solo dance (originally from Cuba) in $\frac{3}{4}$ or $\frac{3}{8}$ time. It is traditionally danced to an Andalusian song with castanet accompaniment and *cachucha* means 'little boat'. Lindsey-Clark is an accomplished guitarist who made his London solo debut at the Wigmore Hall in 1983 at the age of 16. He has also written many compositions for grade exams and this piece is taken from the book *First Repertoire for Guitar, vol. 2*.

The time signature is $\frac{3}{4}$ so remember to accent the first beat to give a lilting feel. Ensure that bass notes are kept sustained but try also to hold the fretted notes where possible, especially the notes in bars 13 and 17 that make up a major second interval. The strummed chords at the end should be slightly spread out but don't drag your finger too much across the strings.

It's Just a Matter of Time (Powlesland)

Nick Powlesland is an experienced guitarist, teacher and composer based in Lancashire. He has written many of the pieces for *The Real Guitar Book vol. 1-3*, several of which have been used for Trinity grades over the years.

It's Just a Matter of Time is great for getting to know the notes on the lower strings and reading below the stave. It has a bit of a blues sound to it and part of the piece uses the 'call and response' pattern which is a common feature in blues. 'Call and response' (or 'question and answer') is where the first phrase (call) is answered by the next phrase (response), like a musical conversation. Keep a strong sense of pulse and make sure the syncopations are played in time without rushing, and all the minims and semibreves are held as they should. As the title suggests: it's all about timing!

Tiny Tango (Tolan)

Gerald Tolan studied at the Royal Academy of Music and released the album *The Romantic Guitar* in 1977. *Tiny Tango* is taken from a collection of 12 easy pieces called *Progressive Pieces*. The tango is a dance form that originated in Argentina and Uruguay around 1880. Tango should be played with passion and energy and have some of the hot-blooded Latin temperament!

There are a lot of chromatic notes and interesting rhythms in this piece. The syncopations can be tricky, especially with the bass notes added, but they are crucial to the tango style. Focus on the melody before adding the bass line and keep the rhythms distinct and accurate throughout. *Tiny Tango* is in $\frac{2}{2}$ and should be played with some pace to avoid sounding heavy or dragging and feel like two beats rather than four. Ensure that your fretting hand fingers are in alignment with the fretboard and close to the string when playing the chromatic notes.

Playing chromatic notes is a good way to improve your hand position, for example if you struggle with your fourth finger being too far away from the string, or if your first finger is leaning too much away from you. As an exercise, try playing chromatically up from fret one and keep all fingers close to the strings all the time, then move to fret two and repeat etc. When you can't go any further, reverse the exercise and play descending starting with finger four. You could also move up more than one fret at a time and practise position change, or just make up your own chromatic exercises along or across strings.

Andante

Edited by Norman Vaux

Ferdinando Carulli
(1770-1841)

Allegro

Mauro Giuliani
(1781-1829)

Andantino

op. 59

Matteo Carcassi
(1792-1853)

Humoresque

Patrick Benham
(b. 1940)

The Hugh Christie Pieces IV

Geoffrey Twigg
(b. 1954)

Cachucha

(Spanish Dance)

Vincent Lindsey-Clark
(b. 1956)

It's Just a Matter of Time

Nick Powlesland
(b. 1965)

Tiny Tango

Gerald Tolan

Teaching Notes – Grade 2

Capriccio from Partita in A Minor (Losy)

A *capriccio* is an Italian term for a lively piece of music, often free in form; partita is an instrumental piece of music for a single instrument. The aristocratic Bohemian baroque composer and lutenist Jan Antonin Losy (Comte d'Logy), was born around 1650 in Steken.

Capriccio is fairly typical of the Baroque style. The voices interweave and overlap throughout and there is plenty to do for both hands. Work through the phrases slowly and gradually build up speed but aim to finish each phrase properly as they dovetail with each other. The fretting hand position must also be quite upright to play some of the lower parts while sustaining a note in the upper part. The dynamic marking is *mf* but this should be taken as a guide only. Music from the Baroque period was often notated without dynamic markings so there is some room for personal interpretation. You could, for example, experiment with dynamic variations and timbre on the repeats.

Etude op. 44 no. 2 (Sor)

Fernando Sor is one of the best known and most significant guitar composers, as well as being regarded as the best guitarist by his contemporaries. He was born in Barcelona in 1778 and though he is best known for his guitar compositions, he also composed for a range of other genres including opera, orchestra and ballet. This *Etude no. 2* is taken from a series of *24 Little Progressive Etudes*, published in 1831.

This étude is in C major and consists of two sections in ABA (ternary) form. The thumb has to move smoothly across the strings for the first two bars, so practise the picking slowly as this is played many times throughout the piece. In fact, there are a lot of repeated phrases so aim for variation in tone and dynamics to give contrast and colour.

Waltz II (Aguado)

Dionisio Aguado was born in Madrid in 1784 and is another major contributor to the classical guitar literature and a good friend of Fernando Sor. Aguado's guitar method *Escuela de Guitarra* was published in 1825 and it is still popular among guitar students today. He also composed numerous waltzes, minuets and other light pieces.

The key of G major is well suited to the guitar with lots of open strings, although there is a brief modulation to A minor in the second half. You can vary the dynamics on the repeat but keep the dotted rhythms accurate and make sure the phrases are separated by the rests.

Tango Pour Mario (Montreuil)

The Canadian composer and multi-instrumentalist Gérard Montreuil wrote a series of pieces for beginners, which were collected in the book *Divertissements pour guitar vol. 1*. The compositions were created to help beginners and facilitate learning the guitar. *Tango Pour Mario* is one of those pieces.

This tango is in A major and has an AABA form. The B section modulates to A minor and the whole piece is based on a two-note chord idea (dyad). There is quite a bit of chromatic movement going on, which creates harmonic tension and release between the upper and lower voice so aim to keep both voices clear and well balanced throughout. The dynamics have been added for contrast and variation but you can make changes on the repeats and feel free to experiment with tone colour to add to your own interpretation.

Cubana (Benham)

Patrick Benham is a British teacher and composer based in Somerset, and *Cubana* is taken from the book *7 Easy Guitar Solos*. Although he has retired from teaching, he still composes for guitar and his work has recently been included on the album *SixDancers*. Benham is also an author and has written the book *Avalonians*.

Cubana is a lively piece in C, in ABA form with a contrasting middle section. The syncopation gives the piece a Latin flavour; try to keep the melody clear and distinct from the accompaniment. You can hold the chords for as long as possible, though it can be a bit of a stretch with the G7 chord in bars 1 and 5. The focus in the middle section shifts to the bass so keep the open G in check and leave finger 3 on the low G throughout. This will also set you up nicely for the last chord in bar 16 before the *D.S. al Coda*.

Taberna Vieja (Schwertberger)

Gerald Schwertberger was an Austrian composer who had a long career teaching and composing for several instruments. Schwertberger worked in Guatamala for a while and *Taberna Vieja* (meaning 'old taverna') is taken from a book called *Latin America*.

This delightful tango in G is full of syncopations which are essential to the style. It has three different sections and the middle section in E minor provides a nice contrast to the gentle G major sections. The bass pattern of root-fifth-octave is typical of the tango style so make sure you keep that distinct and prominent all the time. The ornament in bar 3 is called a *mordent* and should be played rapidly with finger 4. It is technically an *upper mordent* as you are alternating to a higher note but the important thing is to be accurate with the slurs so all the notes can be heard.

New Day (Eythorsson)

Sveinn Eythorsson is an Icelandic guitarist, composer and web developer. He studied guitar in Spain from the age of 17 and now works as a guitar teacher in Iceland where he has also set up an online guitar school. *New Day* is taken from a collection called *9 Easy Guitar Pieces*.

This lovely piece is in ABA form and the melody is clearly defined throughout. The middle section moves up to position III and the D in bar 10 should be played with finger 3 so practise making a smooth transition in bars 10-11. The diminuendo should be gradual. You could also add a short crescendo in bar 16 to build back up to *f* for the repeat or *mf* for the ending.

Peppermint Rag (Cottam)

A 'rag' is short for a musical genre known as ragtime which was popular in the late 19th and early 20th centuries in America and characterised by its syncopated (ragged) rhythm. Ragtime music was often played on the piano with the bass on the strong beats (1 and 3) and chords on the weak beats (2 and 4). *Peppermint Rag* is from the book *Zebramusic for Guitar* by David Cottam, a guitarist and composer from Devon. He has written several pieces for grade exams, as well as recording and performing as a solo guitarist.

This is a fun but challenging piece to play with lots of chromatic movement and syncopations. The thumb has to keep a strong and steady rhythm with an emphasis on beats 1 and 3, and the syncopated chromatic notes must be kept in time so there is a nice interplay between the two voices. The dynamics are guidelines only so feel free to experiment with your own interpretation.

Capriccio

from *Partita in A minor*

Edited by John Cadman

Jan Antonín Losy
(1650–1721)

Etude

op. 44 no. 2

Fernando Sor
(1778-1839)

Waltz II

Dionisio Aguado
(1784-1849)

Tango Pour Mario

Gerard Montreuil
(1927-1991)

Cubana

Patrick Benham
(b. 1940)

Taberna Vieja

Gerald Schwertberger
(1941–2014)

New Day

Sveinn Eythorsson
(b. 1964)

Peppermint Rag

for Fabien Flight

David Cottam